THE ARAB HERITAGE
OF
WESTERN CIVILIZATION

THE ARAB HERITAGE
OF
WESTERN CIVILIZATION

THE LEAGUE OF ARAB STATES
Arab Information Center
747 Third Avenue, New York, N.Y. 10017

First Edition: January 1962
Second Edition: October 1972
Third Edition: April 1974

909.0982
L253a

Contents

41549

List of Illustrations

16—A medical manuscript, originally from the Canon of Avicenna and restored by Mousa ibn Amrani during the Middle Ages.

17—An illustration of medical technique showing a Caesarian section operation. al-Biruni (973-1048 A.D).

18—A portrait of six Greek physicians found in the Arabic translation of Galen's Treatise on Electuaries (1200 A.D.).

19—Avenzoar, (1073-1162 A.D.) an Arab physician who studied carcinoma of the stomach and esophagus.

20—An illustration of three mythological figures from a manuscript by al-Qazwini, 1279 A.D.

21—Details of a window of the Alhambra, Granada.

22—"A couple"—a drawing by Albert Durer (1471-1528).

23—A 13th century illustration of a lady lecturing in a Baghdad mosque.

24—Celebration of the end of Ramadan. Miniature painting by 'al-Wasiti, 1237 A.D.

25—The Saying on Political Wisdom from al-Muquaddimah by ibn Khaldun (1332-1406 A.D.).

26—A page from a copy of the Koran inscribed by Ya'qut al-Mustasimi, 14th century A.D.

27—Hispano-Moresque fabric with calligraphic design from the 15th century.

28—A conception of Archangel Gabriel appearing in a book by al-Qazwini, 1279 A.D.

29—Court of the Lions, Alhambra, Granada.

30—Glass lantern from the mosque of an-Nasir Muhammad, Cairo (1330 A.D.).

31—A chandelier from the mosque of Sultan Hassan, Cairo (1363 A.D.).

8

THE WAY THEY GAVE

IT MAY seem surprising that Christianity, though founded more than six hundred years before Islam, in one important aspect not only followed in the footsteps of Islam, but also found itself deeply indebted to it.

While the spiritual and moral foundation supporting Western civilization is the Christian gospel, it was the legacy of the Greeks that enabled that civilization to make intellectual progress. Our main intellectual and scientific disciplines derive from Aristotle and Plato, Pythagoras, Euclid, Hippocrates and Galen. Yet by the time our Christian foundation was firmly set, our intellectual means were exceedingly weak, and there existed a deep gulf between faith and reason.

It was the Arabs who, in trying to bridge a similar gap, came to our assistance. For, while Europe was ignorant of the Greek legacy, the Arabs discovered it. Their assimilation and distribution of that treasure forms one of the most fascinating chapters in the history of man's quest for knowledge.

Less than a hundred years after the death of the Prophet Muhammad in 632, Islam was firmly established among the Arabs. But, having carved ¬out for themselves one of the world's greatest empires, and having been brought in touch with the more advanced civilizations of the Persians and Byzantines, the Arabs felt the need for a rational interpretation of their faith which left too many questions intellectually unanswered. To find these answers, the Arabs had need of a philosophical discipline and an unassailable logic. The only civilization that had produced both was that of the Greeks.

True enough, there were Greek manuscripts to be found in medieval Europe. But they lay hidden under the dust of monasteries, and their custodians were too ignorant to understand them. Fortunately, a second and more comprehensive reservoir of Greek knowledge existed in the Near East. After Alexander the Great's conquest of that area, that knowledge found a ready welcome throughout the outlying areas of his far-flung empire. Religious schisms had driven out many of the Christian scholars from Constantinople, among whom the most important were the Nestorian Greeks, and Syrians. They found new homes in Mesopotamia and Persia where they translated their Greek manuscripts into Syriac, a language derived from Aramaic. It was that Syriac version that the Arabs were to adopt as their own.

When Mamoun, son of Haroun el Rashid, became Caliph (803 A.D.), the Arabs were fully aware of the Greek heritage, and it was Mamoun's own zest for knowledge that provided the Arab scholars with the springs at which to quench their intellectual thirst. He founded, in Baghdad, a special academy of translators,

Dar el Hikma, at the head of which he placed the Nestorian Christian Hunayn ibn Ishaq. Ibn Ishaq in turn employed Christian, Muslim and Jewish helpers. In an age of national and religious intolerance, the academy provided a revolutionary example of intellectual cooperation on a truly international and inter-religious basis. No field of Greek learning, from philosophy to mathematics, medicine and botany, was neglected.

In the course of their labors, the Arabs did far more than mere translation. They also commented upon, and explained the Greeks, and gradually erected upon the Greek foundations an intellectual edifice of their own. It is due to them that Aristotle, Plato, Euclid, Heraclitus and Galen were salvaged from oblivion, to be passed on eventually to an ignorant Europe. While the initial work was done in the Near East, it was greatly elaborated on by the western Arabs, mainly in Sicily, Spain and Morocco.

1—The reception of the Venetian Ambassador Domenico Trevizano at the palace of Sultan Qansou al-Ghoury in Cairo, 1512. (School of Gentile Bellini.)

After the labors of St. Augustine in the 14th century had brought a brief intellectual dawn, a dark night of ignorance descended upon Europe. Yet gradually Christian thinkers were smitten with problems similar to those which the Arabs had set out to solve at a much earlier date. While they had begun to put their religious tenets on a sound intellectual basis within a hundred years after the death of their Prophet, it took Christendom a thousand years to do the same.

Many of the questions raised by the Christian gospel were similar to those that had puzzled the Muslims, and also awaited a rational interpretation. Did God create the universe out of nothing, or had that universe existed eternally in potentiality? Did He create it directly, or through such intermediaries as the Aristotelian *nous,* the neo-Platonic *logos,* or the hierarchies of archangels and angels? Was the human soul part of a universal soul or was each created *ex nihilo?* And, after death, did that soul survive as an individual entity or did it return to a great *anima mundi?*

By the 13th century some of the more enlightened scholars in Christendom had become aware of the answers to be found in the writings of the Greeks and the Arabs. But to study either of these, the available manuscripts had to be translated from Arabic, for Arabic versions, belonging to both Greeks and Muslims, were the only ones at hand. Even the indispensable commentaries on Aristotle were all the works of Arabs, chiefly of Farabi, Ibn Sina and Ibn Rushd.

When, in the 13th century, Arab civilization had passed its peak in the Near East, it took a new lease on life in the West—that is under the Moors in Spain and Morocco. Some of Islam's greatest thinkers, Ibn Hazm, Ibn Tufail and Ibn Rushd, worked either in the Magh-

12

2—Averroes (1126-1196), ink drawing by Raphael.

reb or in Spain. Spain, while politically almost recon-
quered from the Moors by the Christians, continued to
be—thanks to the former—Europe's chief intellectual
and artistic work shop. Its most influential thinker was
Ibn Rushd, known by the Latins as Averroës. It was
primarily he who revolutionized Christian scholastic-

ism. With his majestic commentaries on Aristotle he provided Europe with its main source for an understanding of the Greek thinker who influenced Western intellectual and scientific development more than any other individual.

Though Western scholars might disagree with this or that Arab doctrine, they could not do without them, for these doctrines contained the chief philosophical, mathematical, astronomical, medical and other scientific tools available at the time. Thanks to these the best minds in Europe gradually developed the attitude of scientific objectivity without which the Renaissance could hardly have come about, preparing the way for Copernicus, Keppler, Galileo, Newton, Descartes and Leibniz.

From Khwarizmi (A.D. 850) Europe learned (though three hundred years later) the Arabic numerals, the science of algebra and the then most valid astronomical tables, translated in Spain by the Englishman Abelard of Bath (1126). Basing his approach on that of the Arabs, the Italian Leonardo Fibonacci (1202) laid the foundations of Western mathematics, without which the work of the later astronomers could not have been accomplished. More or less at the same time, and chiefly in Spain, the writings of Euclid, Ptolemy, Galen, Dioscorides and of the great Arab astronomers, chemists, botanists and cartographers were made available in Latin versions.

The first center of Western, or Latin as they were called, studies of Arab lore was established at Toledo in Spain under Archbishop Raymond, Primate of Spain (1130-50), who set out to make the work of the Arab thinkers available to Christians. He founded a college of translators and put Dominicus Gondisalvi in charge.

3—Arabic motifs and figures on a 13th century German ornamented clock.

Under his direction Aristotle, as interpreted by Farabi and Ibn Sina, was Latinized. The sketchy knowledge of Aristotle as gained independently by Ireland's Celtic church made only a very minor contribution to the West's knowledge of the Greeks. While the Toledan scholars concentrated on philosophy, those working under the auspices of Emperor Frederick II in Sicily undertook Arab sciences as well. To enable Western scholars to learn from the Arabs, Frederick founded, in 1224, the University of Naples.

The focus of Western attention was Ibn Rushd, both as an independent philosopher and Aristotelian and as the author of some of the most influential medical works. Among his keenest followers were the Jews, who called him "the soul and intelligence of Aristotle.' The greatest Jewish philosopher, Ibn Maymun, known as Maimonides (d.1204), was among those responsible for the establishment of an Averroist school, while Samuel ben Tibbon and Moses ben Tibbon translated most of Ibn Rushd's works into Hebrew. The language of the Spanish Jews, both scholars and common folk, was Arabic, just as Jewish philosophy at its highest, that is between the 12th and 14th centuries, derived primarily from the Arabs. In fact the first Hebrew grammar was written in Arabic.

Many of the Christian thinkers placed greater confidence in Ibn Rushd than they did in Aristotle himself. While Albertus Magnus (1206-1280) relied mainly on Farabi's and Ibn Sina's versions of the latter, his pupil St. Thomas of Aquinas was turning more and more to Ibn Rushd in matters philosophical, and to Ghazali in those concerning theology. St. Thomas became Christendom's leading expert on Arab doctrines, and his greatest books, which formed the basis of later Christian theology and philosophy, are impregnated with those doctrines.

Averroism became the chief doctrine of the philosophical schools of Paris, Padua and Bologna, and in Venice it undoubtedly helped to lay the foundations for the Renaissance. In England the chief propagator of Averroism was John Baconthorp, the provincial of the English Carmelites.

Yet another branch of Arab learning that influenced Western progress was medicine. One of Europe's leading medical schools, at Montpellier in France, was founded by Arab doctors driven from Spain. Translations of Ibn Sina's and Ibn Rushd's medical books were being published in Europe until the 17th century.

Viewing the "Arab Transmission" from a perspective of almost a thousand years, we are struck by the extraordinary broadmindedness that the Arabs manifested at a time when the West was rent by inter-racial and inter-denominational strife. There was the constant enmity between Rome and Constantinople, the sacking of the latter city by the Latins, the persecution of minorities and the proponents of new intellectual doc-

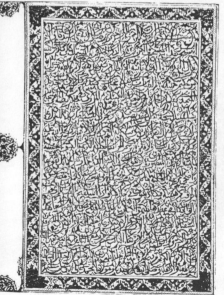 

4—A cover and a page from an ancient copy of the Korán, at the Escorial Library, Spain.

trines, the intolerance towards Muslims and Jews, and the Inquisition in general. It required the example established by the Arabs in employing Christians, Jews, Zoroastrians and Indians in a common search for knowledge to bring about a similar attitude in a Frederick II, a Raymond of Cremona or a Roger Bacon.

It is thus evident that what the Arabs transmitted to the West went far beyond the Greek legacy, Arab learning and the principles of academic objectivity and sound learning. For it was the Arabs from whom Europe also learned that there can be no exclusiveness in man's quest for truth, and that truth itself knows no frontiers of race or religion. These were in fact the principles that were to guide the Renaissance and make Western progress and Western civilization possible.

A PHILOSOPHICAL PASSAGE

A T a time when the theories of Ludwig Wittgenstein and his disciples reduce philosophy to a semantic game of word definitions, attempts to probe what used to be called "the ultimate verities of existence" enjoy little popularity. Yet for more than two thousand years, philosophers considered such truths as God's nature, man's relationship to God, the difference between essence and existence as the very lifeblood of their pursuits. Likewise, the very backbone of scientific investigation, that is logic, was regarded as the proper subject for philosophy, and it was philosophers rather than scientists who passed on to the West the logic of Aristotle—for some two thousand years the decisive tool of scientific research. This tool, however, Western science did not lift directly from Aristotle. For Europe was hardly aware of Aristotle, and knew hardly more about the other intellectual leaders of ancient Greece. After St. Augustine's partial transmission of Plato, Europe remained ignorant of the Greek legacy for almost a thousand years. Yet, while Christianity shaped the spiritual and moral tenets of the Western world, it was the legacy of Greece out of which that world was to

·GALENVS · AVICENA · YPOCRATES

5—Galenus, Avicenna and Hippocrates, the great physicians of antiquity, as they appeared in a 16th-century medical book.

fashion its intellectual personality. Without that legacy there could have been no Keppler, no Copernicus, Leonardo, or Newton, and none of the scientific discovery that has become the trademark of Western civilization.

The story of how the Greek inheritance was salvaged by Nestorian monks who, as refugees from Byzantium, established themselves in Persia, and how the Arabs, translating, interpreting and advancing it, passed it, finally, on to the West, makes one of the most fascinating chapters in the chronicles of man's intellectual progress. For it was the Arabs who, between the 8th and the 12th centuries, were the first to recognize the full significance of the Hellenic heritage, and who, with an astonishing openmindedness, made it their own, thus laying the foundations for Christian scholasticism and, ultimately, for the Renaissance.

The Arabs—a term that in this context denotes all the medieval scholars of Islam, all of whom used the Arabic language and are exponents of Arab culture—came originally to Greek philosophy out of a need to provide rational justifications for religious truths. Faith by itself was not enough: it must conform to reason and withstand an intellectual examination. Thus, from the very early days of Islam, Arab civilization disclosed one of its outstanding features, namely the persistent effort to integrate faith with reason, the spiritual with the material, and to avoid the split between the two, a split that was responsible for the divorce between science and morality in the West. Basing themselves mainly on Aristotle (and, to a lesser extent, on Plotinus), the Arab philosophers found the means for explaining away such troublesome problems as those of the unity of God and the multiplicity of the universe, of God's perfection and the latter's imperfections, of the evolutionary process that led from God, via the First Cause or the Logos and the Universal Soul, to the world of matter. In that process they inevitably had to deal with a number of questions that today would be considered as belonging to the domain of science rather than of philosophy, such as the nature of matter or of time, and the interrelation between time, mass and movement. They also made startling discoveries about the processes of the mind.

That many of their findings were superseded by later investigations does not diminish the value of their pioneering work, and modern Western scholarship has acknowledged that the Christian scholars who made the coming of the Renaissance possible stood on the shoulders of their Arab predecessors.

It would take an entire volume to demonstrate the pervasive influence of Arab philosophy upon Western scholasticism. It may, however, suffice to mention a few of the greatest medieval thinkers who, besides giving Christian theology its rational justification, provided Europe with the logic and the intellectual tools without which the Renaissance would have been greatly retarded. The outstanding figure was obviously St. Thomas Aquinas, Christianity's greatest apologist and philosopher. Now it was Avicenna (Ibn Sina), the tenth cent. philosopher and scientist, who in his doctrine on essence and existence presented the *Doctor Angelicus,* as indeed the entire 13th cent., with the starting point for the West's philosophical development. Avicenna, in the words of Roger Bacon, *dux et princeps philosophiae,* is the one whom St. Thomas invokes continuously in his *De Ente et Essentia,* whom he places side by side with Plato, and some of whose fundamental theories, such as that on form and matter, he incorporates in his doctrine. St. Thomas is similarly influenced by Farabi (died 950) from whom he actually lifts entire passages, and by one of Islam's greatest philosopher-mystics, Ghazali (died 1111). Though he was opposed to the doctrine of the soul of the great Moorish philosopher Averroës (Ibn Rushd, d. 1198), he accepted the latter as the most authoritative commentator of Aristotle.

Both Christian and Jewish scholars saw in Averrëes the greatest luminary since Aristotle, and soon Averroism was to sweep Europe. It became, in fact, quite as much the academic 'fashion' (though with far more lasting consequences) as Existentialism did after the Second World War and Wittgenstein in more recent years. Starting from Morocco and Moorish Spain and reaching, across Italy, most countries of Europe, Arab

22

philosophy, both pure and as a transmitter of Greek thought, became, in the 11th and 12th centuries, the West's main intellectual discipline. Until the 16th cent. Latin versions of the Arab philosophers remained required subjects at the universities of Bologna, Padua, Montpellier, Paris and Oxford. Special schools of translators were founded in Spain with the sole object of rendering those philosophers into Latin versions. Though the Church considered Averroism a heresy, Western scholars accepted it avidly, and Averroism became the chief incentive for a scholasticism intellec-

6—A library in Baghdad in the 13th century. Illustrated by al-Wasiti, 1237 A.D.

tually independent and divorced from theology. Though Avicenna's influence was less widespread, it may have penetrated even more deeply. Under its impact even the teachings of St. Augustine became transformed into what came to be known as Avicennaist Augustinianims. Even for Christian scholars most opposed to the Arab doctrines these turned into one of the chief fertilizing forces.

Among those whose decidedly Christian doctrines are strongly colored by Arab philosophy we find not

7—Lecture given by a scholar in Baghdad (13th century. Illustration by al-Wasiti), 1237 A.D.

only St. Thomas but likewise his famous teacher Albertus Magnus (d. 1280), the first to adopt in its entirety 'Arabian logic,' actually the logic of Aristotle as formulated by Avicenna, a logic that was to affect so profoundly Western scientific development.

Then there were Roger Bacon at Oxford (d. 1294), one of the most enthusiastic disciples of the Arabs, and William of Auvergne (d. 1249), the great teacher at the University of Paris, who identifies himself far more with the Islamic philosophers than he does with St. Augustine. John Baconthrop (d. 1346), the provincial of the English Carmelites, became known as the 'Prince of Averroists', and, in the year in which America was discovered, the general of the Servits ordered the publication of Averroës' great commentary. As late as 1552 an even more complete edition of Averroës appeared in Padua. In 1473 Louis XI of France laid down that Aristotle was to be taught with the commentaries of Averroës.

Equally avid for Arab philosophical lore were the Jewish scholars. In fact Jewish intellectual progress owed its entire existence to the Arabs, for only in Arab countries did the Jews enjoy freedom, and Jewish scholars worked under the patronage of Arab princes. Without these favorable conditions and without the inspiration of Arab philosophy, there might never have been a Maimonides, a Yehuda ben Solomo Cohen, an Avicebron, a Levi ben Gerson. Practically all these Jewish thinkers, the main glory of Jewish philosophy, used Arabic as their language. The Jews became among the chief transmitters (and translators) of Arab philosophy and were among the most enthusiastic Averroists.

Though for political (and denominational) reasons European post-Renaissance scholars kept silent about their indebtedness to the Arabs, by the end of the 19th cent., Western orientalists had acquired sufficient objectivity to admit it openly. They also acknowledged the fact that the pro-Hellenic force that gave the Renaissance its main impetus had been generated by the Arabic studies of the 12th and 13th centuries. Europe's own and later archeological and artistic discoveries of Greece merely complemented a tendency that proved decisive for the shape Western civilization was to take.

THEY OFFERED A ZERO

Even a schoolboy knows that the numerals in which the score is given in a football game are called Arab numerals. He probably assumes that these have always been in use. In actual fact Europe took them over from the Arabs only in the thirteenth century, fighting their introduction and that of the decimal system that went with them for several hundred years, thus depriving itself of the advantages of one of the world's greatest scientific contributions. Prior to the Arab numerals, the West relied upon the clumsy system of Roman numerals. Whereas in the decimal system, the number 1848 can be written in four figures, in the Roman numerals, eleven figures are needed, and this will be the result: MDCCCXLVIII. It is obvious that even for the solution of the simplest arithmetical problem, Roman numerals called for an enormous expenditure of time and labor. The Arab numerals, on the other hand, render even complicated mathematical tasks relatively simple. The West's scientific advance would have been impossible had scientists continued to depend upon the Roman numerals, and been deprived of the wonderful simplicity and flexibility of the decimal system and its main glory, the little naught that we call zero. Though the Arab numerals were originally a Hindu invention, it was the Arabs who turned them into a workable system, and the earliest Arab zero we have knowledge of dates from the year 873, whereas the earliest Hindu zero is dated 876. For the subsequent four hundred years, Europe laughed at a method that depended upon the use of the zero, "a meaningless nothing."

Had the Arabs given us nothing but the decimal system, their contribution to progress would have been considerable. In actual fact they gave us infinitely more.

It has become the fashion to claim that religion is an impediment to scientific advance. The scientific accomplishments of the Arabs — the term "Arab" being applied to all scholars who, even if not actually Arab, used Arabic as their language and were the product of the specifically Arab civilization—suggest that it need not be so. What, in the West, often handicapped scientific progress was not religion but a narrowly dogmatic interpretation of religious truths by conservative church authorities, of which the persecution of a Galileo and the burning of witches are but a few examples. Most of the mathematical discoveries of the Arabs came about not in spite of religion but because of religion. Likewise, it was religion that induced Arab scientists not to limit themselves to one particular field but to become universalists.

In Islam, the religion of most Arabs, there was less of the separation between the spiritual and the material than there was in the West. For the Muslims the material universe was but the visible "cloak" of God, and in order to understand God's nature it was necessary to investigate all the aspects of his outer "appear-

8—A 16th century print of the Arab astronomer Abulmusar
(787-886 A.D.).

ance," as manifested in the visible world. Thus a mathematician would usually also be a theologian, an astronomer, a geographer, a physician, and something of a philosopher. Because of his universalism, Leonardo da Vinci is rightly regarded as one of the most glorious figures of the Renaissance. He was not only a painter and a sculptor but also an architect, a physicist and an inventor. He is perhaps the outstanding representative of the Renaissance universalism that replaced the narrow scholasticism of the Middle Ages. In actual fact, the "universalist genius" is not a product of the Renaissance but had been anticipated several hundred years earlier by the great Arab scientists.

The men who advanced Western mathematical and astronomical knowledge sufficiently to enable us today to send rockets to the moon were Keppler, Copernicus, Galileo and Newton. Yet none of these could have arrived at his scientific conclusions had it not been for the spadework done several hundred years earlier by the Arab mathematicians and astronomers. George Sarton, the great Harvard historian of science, wrote in his monumental *Introduction to the History of Science*: "From the second half of the eighth to the end of the eleventh century, Arabic was the scientific, the progressive language of mankind . . . When the West was sufficiently mature to feel the need of deeper knowledge, it turned its attention first of all, not to Greek sources, but to the Arabic ones." And Briffault wrote in his *Making of Humanity*: "Investigation, accumulation of positive knowledge, minute methods of science and pro-

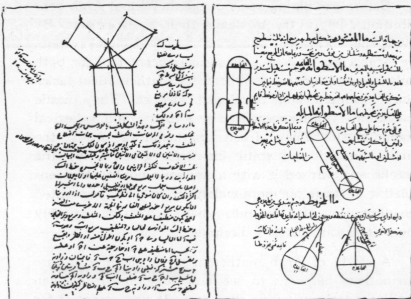

9—Pages from al-Biruni's (973-1048) manuscript on the elements of astronomy (left), and Tabit ibn Qarra's translation of Euclid, 890 A.D.

longed observation were alien to the Greek temperament. These were introduced to Europe by the Arabs. European science owes its existence to the Arabs."

It was in the twelfth century that Europe became aware of the scientific achievements of the Arabs, and began to translate their works. Archbishop Raymond founded a special college of translators at Toledo in Spain, and it was there, and in other centers, that some of the great Christian scholastics, Archdeacon Gondisalvi, Robert of Chester, Michael Scot, Gerard of Cremona translated most of the Arabic works on mathematics and astronomy. In most European universities Arab works formed the basis of mathematical studies, and we find these reflected in the writings of Leonardo da Vinci, Leonardo Fibonacci of Pisa, and Master Jacob of Florence.

Before examining some of the individual Arab contributions, let us try to define their chief aspects. By giving the world their numerals and the decimal system, the Arabs provided us with a magnificent tool for both daily use and for the most complex mathematical tasks. They invented and developed algebra. They made revolutionary advances in trigonometry and spherical trigonometry. They freed mathematics from the earlier limited and static character given it by the Greeks and infused it with a dynamic quality that enabled it to range far more widely, and that incorporated the dimension of Time into what used to be a purely one-or-two dimensional discipline.

A study of Arab mathematics—a pastime of rare fascination—helps us to see how religious beliefs can fertilize purely scientific discovery. It was essential for the Arabs to obtain a more precise knowledge of astronomy (and geography) than was available in the

10—Front and back views of an ancient Arab astrolabe.

early Middle Ages. For a Muslim is enjoined to perform a number of religious observances that have distinctly astronomico-geographical implications. When he says his prayers, he must face Mecca; if he wishes to perform the pilgrimage to Mecca, he must first know in what direction and what distance he will have to travel. Yet a thousand years ago such a journey might take months or even years, for the would-be-pilgrim might be living in Spain, in Sicily or in Asia Minor, all of these forming parts of the medieval Arab Empire. During Ramadan, the month of the yearly fast, when between sunrise and sunset he has to abstain from food and other gratifications of the senses, he must know in advance the precise moment when the moon rises at night and sets in the early morning. All these functions required a detailed knowledge of astronomy and geography. It was thus under the great Khalif Mamoun (813-833) that the Arabs set out upon their astronomical investigations. Mamoun — a son of Haroun al Rashid of "Arabian Nights" fame — built a special observatory at Palmyra, and gradually his scientists determined the length of a degree, thus establishing longitude and latitude.

Among the Arabs who laid the foundations for modern astronomy the two leading ones were Battani and Biruni. Battani's (858-929) astronomical tables were not only taken over avidly by the West, but were in use there until the Renaissance. He was the first one to replace the Greek chord by the sine, in trigonometry. His works were translated and published in Europe from the twelfth until the mid-sixteenth century.

Professor Sarton considers Biruni (973-1048) "one of the very greatest scientists of all time." It was he who gave, finally, an accurate determination of latitude and longitude, and who, six hundred years before Galileo, discussed the possibility of the earth's rotation round its own axis. He also investigated the relative speeds of sound and light. Not limiting himself to mathematics and astronomy, he also succeeded in determining the specific density of 18 precious stones and minerals.

Because of the Koran's very concrete prescriptions regarding the division of an estate among the children of a deceased person, it was incumbent upon the Arabs to find the means for very precise delineations of lands. Let us say a father left a piece of land 17 acres large and very irregularly shaped to his six sons, each one of whom had to receive precisely one sixth of his legacy. The mathematics that the Arabs had inherited from the Greeks made such a division extremely complicated, if not impossible. It was the search for a more accurate, more comprehensive and more flexible method that led Khwarizmi (d. 850) to the invention of algebra. According to the leading authority on the subject (Sarton), Khwarizmi "influenced mathematical thought to a greater extent than any other medieval writer." Both algebra, in the true sense of that term, and the term itself (al-jabr) we owe to him. It was he who adopted the Hindu numerals, and, apart from mathematics, he did pioneer work in the fields of astronomy, geography and the theory of music.

Viewed from a distance of over a thousand years, Khwarizmi's algebra is inevitably limited; yet it laid down the first solid basis for later developments in that field. It was thanks to another exponent of Arab civilization, Omar Khayyam (1040-1123), that algebra made an enormous leap forward. Known in the West as the author of the *Rubayat,* a poem made famous by Edward Fitzgerald's translation, he was admired in the East mainly as a methematician. In his use of analytical geometry, he anticipated the geometry of Descartes. Commissioned by the Seljuq Sultan Halikshah to reform the Persian calendar, he prepared a calendar said to be more accurate than the Gregorian in use to the present day. For whereas ours leads to an error of 1 day in 3,300 years, in Omar Khayyam's calendar that error is 1 day in 5,000 years.

However much astronomy depends upon mathematics, equally vital to it are instruments, and in that field too the Arabs proved themselves the chief pioneers. Now in the early Middle Ages there obviously existed no telescopes, electrical gadgets nor radar, and measurements had to be made with purely mechanical instruments, such as the quadrant, the sextant or the astrolabe. To reduce the margin of error, the Arabs made their instruments bigger than any known before, and with their help obtained remarkably accurate results. The most famous observatory at which these instruments were being used was at Maragha, in the thirteenth century, where distinguished astronomers from many countries collaborated, not only Muslim, Christian and Jew, but even Chinese. It was these latter who were responsible for the otherwise surprising appearance of Arab trigonometry in China. Among the leading instrument makers were the ninth century Farghani, who wrote the first comprehensive textbook on astronomy, and Zarkali, the eleventh century author of astronomical tables that became the basis of European research for a long time to come.

It has already been indicated that, in the hands of the Arabs, mathematics acquired a new "dynamic" quality. We find this in Biruni's trigonometry, where numbers become elements of function, and in Khwar-

11—Arab astronomers from Macrobius, as pictured in a Venetian book published about 1513 A.D.

izmi's algebra, where the algebraic symbols contain within themselves potentialities of the infinite. What is significant about this development is that it reveals an intuitive correspondence between mathematics and religion. The Koran presents the universe not as finally created, a finished "article." God keeps re-creating it at every moment of existence. In other words, creation is an ever-living process, and the world is not static but dynamic. This dynamic character, inherent in Islam, is brought out beautifully in Arab mathematics.

Summing up, we might say that the Arab mathematicians, besides passing on to the West the Hindu and Greek legacies, have developed most branches of trigonometry and astronomy, have given us algebra, have invented many astronomical instruments, and have shown that science, instead of being a denial of faith, can be its affirmation.

ROADBOOK TO ATLAS

ONE day, in 1520, Italian sea pirates captured Hassan al Wazzan, a young Arab, twenty-five years old. So deeply were they impressed by his geographical knowledge that eventually he was brought to the Vatican before Pope Leo X, a scion of the great Medici family, made particularly famous as the patron of Michelangelo and Raphael. The Pope, too, was greatly impressed by the young Arab's learning. He persuaded him to become a Christian, and as a token of his appreciation of the young man's qualities, gave him his own name, Leo. Henceforth the convert became known as Leo Africanus, the second part of his name being a tribute to his accomplishments as the greatest geographer of Africa. Of Moorish origin, but born, in 1495, in Granada, and educated in Fez, Leo set out on his African travels at an early age, and, by the time he was captured, was already the greatest expert on the then almost unknown 'black' continent. At the Pope's instigation, he wrote an account of his travels and himself translated it, in 1526, from the original Arabic into Italian. The book was instantly accepted throughout the world as the first authoritative account of Africa, and editions in various European languages succeeded one another in the manner of a modern best seller. For some two hundred years this work remained Europe's chief source of knowledge on Africa. Its author, however, did not remain in Europe but returned to North Africa, reentered the folds of Islam, and died in Tunis in 1550.

Leo Africanus is only the last in the long line of distinguished Arab geographers who have contributed greatly to our knowledge of the world. The nature both of Islam and of the extent of the Arab empire was responsible for the many Arab works on geography. The first incentive behind these was the pilgrimage to Mecca. Just as a medieval Christian was hoping to pray at the Church of the Holy Sepulchre in Jerusalem, so every Muslim attempted to perform the pilgrimage to Mecca. Yet, while the Christians all lived within the comparatively narrow compass of Europe, an Arab might be living many thousands of miles away from Mecca, north, south, east or west from it. To reach his holy city he had to pass through many foreign lands, and thus needed some knowledge of these. In order to assist him on his journey, many of his predecessors compiled detailed records of their travels to Mecca, known as road books. The Arab Empire stretched from India to the Atlantic, and, from the incentive of religion, many Arabs were eager to visit its various parts. With the Arabs' proverbial curiosity and zest for knowledge, many of these travelers recorded what they had seen and experienced on their journeys, producing thus an enormous amount of geographical data.

None of these travelers surpassed in zest and industry Ibn Battuta, considered by modern scholars as the greatest traveler of medieval times, not excluding Marco Polo, Ibn Battuta's senior by twenty years.

Ibn Battuta was born in Tangier in 1304. After completing his studies, he set out on his first journey in 1325 to perform the Pilgrimage, *Al Hajj*. In actual fact the Pilgrimage became but the first stage in a journey across half the world and lasting twenty-four years. Soon after his return to Morocco, in 1349, he left again, staying away till 1354. Appointed kadi (judge) of Fez, he spent the remaining twenty-three years of his life compiling the account of his travels, one of the most comprehensive and, incidentally, most entertaining travel books ever written. Besides visiting all the Arab countries, he went to Turkey, Bulgaria and southern Russia, Persia, and Central Asia. In India, where he spent several years, he was appointed, first, kadi of Delhi, and then ambassador to the Emperor of China. In China, too, he traveled incessantly, going as far north as Peking and as far south as Canton. On his return journey he visited all the North African countries. His second journey took him through Spain and many parts of western Africa, including Timbuctu, Mali, and the Niger region.

Though Ibn Battuta was not a professional geographer, he collected so vast an amount of geographical data that he is acknowledged as one of the leading geographers of all time. Altogether he must have covered some 75,000 miles, and this at a time when horse, camel and sailing boat provided the sole means of transport. Besides geographical information he gives us details of the politics, administration, social conditions and economics of all the countries he visited. He even affords us an intimate insight into the life of women, a subject that was practically tabu to all other globetrotters. By no means indifferent to feminine charms, and following the custom of the times, he contracted a number of marriages in various parts of the world, and thus became something of an expert on the fair sex. Keenly interested in religion, he sought everywhere the company of theologians, scholars and saintly men, finally giving us an invaluable record of the religious life in the fourteenth century. Some of the countries described by him had never been reflected in the writings of either Eastern or Western geographers. At first, his veracity was doubted by his readers, but eventually his account was found to be truthful. He shared the fate of Marco Polo: both described facts that were stranger than fiction, and both had to face a like incredulity.

It was only in the nineteenth century that Western scholars became aware of Ibn Battuta's great book, called *Rihla* (Journey). Since then, however, it has appeared in many different languages. In 1929, Professor H. A. R. Gibb published an abbreviated edition of it, but he is currently working on a translation of all four volumes.

The *Rihla* was by no means the first Arab work containing details on India, China or Russia. Early in the tenth century, Abu Zaid gave the first accounts of India and China, the most important before Marco Polo. In 921, the Abbasid Khalif Maqtadir sent Ibn Fadlan on a mission to the Bulgarian king, and, as a result, we have the earliest trustworthy account of that country and of Russia.

By the twelfth century Europe began to recognize the superiority of Arab learning, including geography. Yet since the countries about which Europeans wished to learn seldom were the same that the Arabs explored

12—The start of a caravan. Illustration by al-Wasiti, 1237 A.D.

and described, the impact of Arab geography upon Europe was less pronounced than was that of Arab mathematics and astronomy. Modern Western scholars, both American and European, now acknowledge that the accounts of Muslim pilgrims were superior to those of European pilgrims, and they dismiss most of these latter as 'childish'. They emphasize the scientific value of the itineraries and road books produced by such Muslim globetrotters as Ibn Jubair of Valencia, the Moroccan Muhammad ibn Rushaid, and the Persian al Harawi. Many of the Arab travelers turned their attention particularly to botanical lore, and, in that process, greatly enlarged the world's knowledge of plants previously unknown. The greatest of these geographer-botanists was Ibn Baitar of Malaga (d. 1248), regarded as the leading botanist of the Middle Ages.

The outstanding names among Arab geographers, however, are those of Masudi, Idrisi and Yakuth. The tenth century Masudi from Baghdad compiled a historic-geographical encyclopedia that, in its painstaking accumulation of the most diverse information, was unique. Besides geographical facts it contained also much information about other sciences, and even a primitive theory of evolution.

Surpassing all other Western and Eastern geographers of the time was Idrisi, born in 1100 in Ceuta in Morocco. When the Norman king Roger II decided to commission the compilation of a world atlas, he chose none of the Western scholars but invited the Muslim Arab Idrisi to his capital in Palermo. The result of that visit was the book *al Kitab al Rujari* (Roger's Book), the best description of the world in medieval times. It contained information on both Christian and Muslim countries. Its chief value derived from its 70 maps, some of which delineate areas previously never chartered. Idrisi also prepared for the king a faplanisphere in silver. Other Arabs gained renown by fashioning beautiful astrolabes in silver or other metal. Many of these precursors of the compass were sought not only for their scientific value but likewise as works of art.

Abdallah Yaqut (1179-1229) attained fame as the author of one of the earliest geographical dictionaries. Enslaved in his youth, he was eventually set free by his master, a merchant from Baghdad. After extensive travels, he wrote his geographical dictionary which, in true universalist tradition of Arab scholars, is not limited to just one branch of learning. It deals also with astronomy, mathematics, grammar and history, and includes even biographies of learned men. Arranged alphabetically with an almost pedantic attention to detail, the dictionary is really a forerunner of the encyclopedias that we are wont to regard as the invention of eighteenth century French scholars. Whereas in the Arab world Yaqut's book has always been admired as one of the ornaments of Arab literature, modern scholars in the West consider it as one of the most important geographical works of the Middle Ages.

Because so much of Arab geographical knowledge derived from travelers rather than from trained geographers, there was little coordination between them and Arab astronomers. So long as the travelers limited themselves to factual descriptions of what they saw they were reliable. But when they branched out into theory they often accepted legend and fable as fact. They based themselves on outdated doctrines of Ptolemy or of Persian-Babylonian geographers whose theories had been disproved by Arab astronomers. Thus

13—Map of the world based on al-Idrisi's map as illustrated in al-Muqqadimah by Ibn Khaldoun (1332-1406 A.D.).

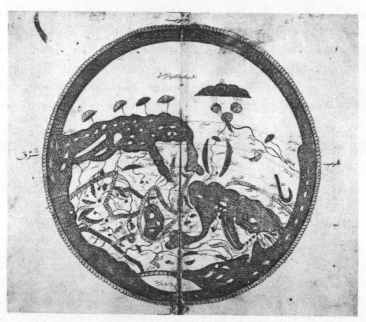

they adhered to the doctrine of the earth's division into seven climates, and treated Asia as an eastern extension of Africa. While, unlike their European colleagues, they no longer believed in a flat earth but accepted its circular shape, they often were fascinated by theories that were completely unscientific. Yet one such theory was to prove of the greatest significance in geographical discovery. This was the doctrine of the 'cupola of Arin' or the world summit, situated supposedly at the center of the world and located somewhere in India. (According to other Arab theorists, the center of the world was at Mecca.) Taken over by such leading Western scholars as Abelard of Bath, Roger Bacon, and Albertus Magnus, the 'Cupola' doctrine found its way into the book *Imago Mundi,* published in 1410 by Cardinal Peter of Ailly. Basing himself on this book, Christopher Columbus assumed that the world was shaped in the form of a pear, and that there must be a second world center in the western hemisphere, forming the base of that pear. In fact he was hoping to find that center when he set out on his momentous journey west. Thus, as the great Dutch orientalist J. H. Kramers points out, 'Islamic geographical theory may claim a share in the discovery of the new world!'

Seafaring owes another debt to Arab geography, or, to be more precise, to Arab navigational knowledge. As is known, it was Vasco de Gama who, in 1498, first found the way to India. When, after circumnavigating Africa, he reached Malindi on Africa's eastern coast, it was his Arab pilot, Ahmad ibn Majid, who showed him the way, thus opening this important route to Western seafarers. The pilot was in the possession of an excellent map prepared by Arabs and unknown in Europe, and he navigated with the help of maritime instruments of which the West was still completely ignorant.

Geography and geographical exploration always fascinated the Arabs. As early as the ninth century, Abbasid Caliphs already contemplated piercing the isthmus of Suez, thus anticipating de Lesseps, the builder of the Suez Canal, by almost a thousand years. The technical difficulties proved, however, too great, and the Abbasid project was never put into effect.

Motivated at first by purely religious considerations and attempts merely to produce helpful guide books for pilgrims setting out for Mecca, the Arabs greatly enlarged our knowledge of geography and made important contributions to the science of navigation.

FROM RAZI TO PASTEUR

WHEN we speak of Arab medicine we do not necessarily mean that all its representatives were Arab. It was the peculiar genius of the Arab civilization that it attracted and encompassed people of many races and creeds, Persians and Syrians, Christians and Jews. Citizens of the Arab Empire, they identified themselves with the Arab-Islamic civilization, and it was the Arabic language, with its great wealth, flexibility and pithiness, that made of them the exponents of that civilization. Between the 8th and the 12th centuries Arabic was as much the universal language of culture, diplomacy and the sciences as Latin was to become in the Middle Ages. If you wanted to read Aristotle, use medical terms, solve a mathematical problem or embark upon a learned discourse, you had to know Arabic.

Some of the great figures in Arab medicine were of Persian descent, yet they all wrote in Arabic and derived their knowledge from books written in Arabic. The development, nay, the very creation of European medicine is unthinkable without the Arab contribution.

For its basis was the legacy of the ancient Greeks, and that legacy was unknown to Europe until the moment when it became available in Arabic translations and with the commentaries of Arab scholars. The first contribution of the Arabs to Western medicine is thus the transmission of Greek knowledge. Between 800 and 900 A.D. they had discovered, translated, commented upon, and assimilated the entire Greek heritage in practically all branches of science. Of medical works they translated not only those of such giants as Hippocrates and Galen, but also of Dioscorides, Paul of Ægina, Oribasius and Rufus of Ephesus.

Arab interest in medicine does not begin with the period when Arab medicine proper made its appearance. Even at the time of the Prophet Muhammad it was not confined to the famous medical school at Jundi-Shapur in Persia. In the most authoritative collection of the Hadith (traditions pertaining to the Prophet), namely that of al Bukhari, we find at the beginning of the fourth volume two books dealing with medicine. Besides counsels of a purely spiritual kind, Muhammad also speaks of such typically Arab remedies as cautery, cupping and the administration of honey; the diseases he refers to include migraine, ophthalmia, pleurisy, leprosy and pestilence. The Prophet advises his followers to refrain from visiting a country where pestilence is raging, this possibly being the first, however inexplicit, recognition of contagion. The first Arab doctor of whom we have documented knowledge was al Harith ibn Kalada, a contemporary of the Prophet and an alumnus of the school at Jundi-Shapur.

Islamic literature, both Arab and Persian, abounds in stories and anecdotes of a medical nature, affirming the great interest taken in things medical. Particularly

47

وَلَيْسَتْ لَمْغَايِلَهُ مُوَافِقٌ لِلْمَثَانَهِ وَالْكُلَا عَ عَ عَ
.: صَنْعُهُ شَرَابِ لِلزُّكَامِ وَالسُّعَالِ :.

14—Physician preparing medicine. From a manuscript of the Materia Medica, 1222-1223 A.D.

popular were the stories that dealt not with what might be called "straight" medicine, but with what Razi termed "ilaj-i-nafsani," or psychotherapeusis, that is cures affected by suggestion and by psychological methods, such as provoking the patient's anger, mirth or shock. Some of the methods employed by Ibn Sina merit the name of psychoanalysis, for the therapy he sometimes applied consisted of leading his patient back to some early recollection of a long forgotten incident that, planted in the unconscious, became the cause of an ailment physical in its nature yet psychological in its origin.

Muslim doctors also made much use of a patient's faith. Since in Islam faith dominated both the sciences of the learned and the lives of common folk, doctors never forgot the unity of the spiritual and the material, and would take refuge as much in the religious forces animating their patients as in biological and physiological resources. Thus our present-day division between what we regard as legitimate medicine, psychoanalysis and faith-healing did not exist in Arab medicine, just as Islamic science seldom was separated from either philosophy or religion. God, the supernatural, the heavens, as in fact the entire universe, were seldom absent from a doctor's considerations. As in mathematics and astronomy, so in Arab medicine religion proved not an impediment to progress but a strong ally.

The superiority of Arab medicine over European was manifested strikingly on occasions when Arab and 'Frankish' doctors worked side by side, as they did in Syria in the days of the Crusades. During lulls between wars there used to be much friendly intercourse between Christians and Arabs, and it was during such lulls that many a Christian prince sought the services of Arab doctors. The therapy of their Christian colleagues more often than not led to death, which was hardly surprising in view of the methods they were wont to apply. The most popular remedy for a wound in an arm or leg was the axe, with which the afflicted limb would be chopped off, leading, if not to instantaneous death, to extinction preceded by gangrene. For other ailments the common method consisted of the shaving of the head, the deep incision of a cross in the flesh of the ailing part, and the exorcism of the devil. This method proved quite as efficacious as did the 'surgeon's' axe. No wonder the Arab doctors came to look down upon the noble art of surgery. On their part they treated their patients according to the vast knowledge they had acquired from Greek, Indian and Arab sources. "To the Arabs, as we can well understand," writes the great English orientalist E. G. Browne, "Frankish medicine appeared most barbarous and primitive compared with their own."

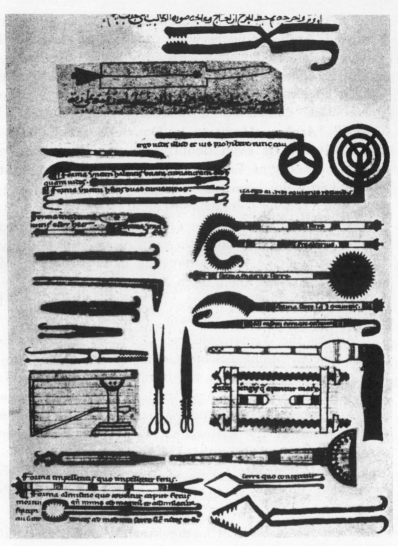

15—Surgical instruments, as illustrated in al-Zahrawi's (d. 1036 A.D.)
Surgical Treatise.

Gradually, however, in western Europe, chiefly in
Spain and Sicily, both strongly subject to Arab influences, scholars were absorbing the knowledge opened
up to them by the Arabs. They approached that knowledge "with a great and growing enthusiasm combined

with a blind trust in its authority. Medieval Europe regarded Arab medicine with superstitious awe, and Cordova was looked upon with admiration by the educated Europeans . . . As a result, up to the end of the sixteenth century, the medical curricula of European universities demanded a knowledge of Avicenna's Canon". (*Arabian Medicine,* by Donald Campbell, London, 1926). It is even doubtful whether the leading medical schools of Europe would have seen the light of day had it not been for the impetus of Arab learning. When such schools were established in Paris (1110 A.D.), Bologna (1113), Montpellier (1181), Padua (1222), and Naples (1224), their curricula were dominated entirely by Arab medicine. It is interesting to note that these universities, owing their birth as they did to Arab influences, have remained among the leading medical schools to the present moment.

Among the Western pioneers of Arab medicine were Roger Bacon, Michael Scott, Gerard of Cremona, Adelard of Bath, and Gerbert, the future Pope Sylvester II. The first transmitter of Arab medicine, however, was a North African, Constantinus Africanus (1820-87), the first to translate the writings of Haly Abbas and other Arab doctors, as well as the Arabic versions of Hippocrates and Galen, into Latin. Pressure from the Church compelled him to suppress the names of the Arab authors.

That the services of medical men were appreciated by the Arabs we learn from innumerable stories that tell us of the lavish gifts showered upon this or that doctor. The Abbasid court physician, Bukht-Yishu, received from public funds a monthly salary of 10,000 dirhams, and from the Privy Purse 50,000 per year. For bleeding the Caliph Harun al Rashid twice a year he received 100,000 dirhams, and an equal sum for administering a biennial purgative draught. From courtiers he received 400,000 per year, and from the Prime Minister's family 1,400,000. Altogether, during 23 years' service, he was paid 88,800,000 dirhams, which roughly corresponds to $25 million. Though his case obviously was not typical, it was by no means unique.

The first great Muslim doctor was the 9th century Bakr Muhammad ibn Zakariya of Ray, known as Razi by the Arabs and as Rhazes by Medieval Europe, universally considered one of the outstanding authorities in medical history. The author of over 20 books, he was the first to diagnose and to describe correctly measles and smallpox. His most important work was the *Hawi,* an extremely detailed medical encyclopedia in 25 volumes that was being used by doctors and students not only in the East, but also throughout Europe.

The second largest medical encyclopedia produced by a Muslim was the *Canun* of Ibn Sina, or Avicenna, the most renowned of all Islamic philosopher-scientists. Precocious almost beyond belief, Ibn Sina did not turn to medicine until he was sixteen, by which time he had already mastered Muslim law, philosophy, natural sciences, and mathematics. He was only eighteen when his fame as a doctor was such as to induce ruling princes to seek his services. A busy statesman, a teacher and lecturer, a profound thinker, a poet, and a highly prolific writer on subjects as diverse as geology, music and mathematics, Ibn Sina treated medicine as only one of his numerous preoccupations. Nevertheless, he produced sixteen books on medicine, including the *Canun, a* work of one million words. This encyclopedia deals with every then known disease, treatment and medication as prescribed by both Greek and Arab authorities, and is generally regarded as the final codification of all Greco-Arab medicine. Some 30 editions of it were issued in

والبقعة المصافية لخط المشرق استواء إنما تسامت
فيها الشمس الدوائر إياما ظلالهم يستاقدون رعمع
المراد بالميل
الاعتدال الدائم
مالعمل
لأن تزايد أجزاء عند العقد تبين أعظم كثيرا
من مزايدها عند المنقلبين على ما هو مبين وعند
المنقلبين حركة أيام ملته أو أربعة أو اكثر
منها أثر محسوس شاءم أن الشمس لبثت هناك
جيئها واحد متقارب مدة معينة فيمن والحيطان
نحبان بعتقد من هذا أن البلاد التي عرضها
مقاربة
متقاربة لليل كله هن أسخن البلاد وبعدها ما
يكون بعده عنه في الجانبين القطبيين مقارب الحمى
عشر درجة ولا يكون الحر في خط المستوي إلى
المفرط الذي يوجبه المسامتة في قريب مدا أقر
وأمر السرطان وللمعمورة للحر البرد في البلاد
المتباعدة عن هذا البلاد الى الشمال البثت هذا ما
يوجب اعتبار عروض المساكن على انها على ب

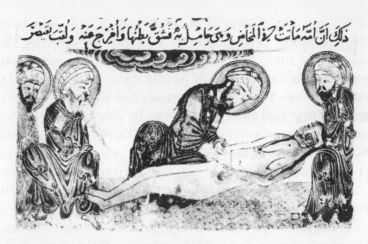

ذلك إن أمّه ماتت حرة الخامس وهي حامل به مشق بطنها وأخرج حيّه ولبث يقظ

17—An illustration of medical technique showing a Caesarian section
operation. al-Biruni (973-1048 A.D.).

Latin, and several in Hebrew. It formed one half of the medical curricula at European universities throughout the fifteenth century. While it is debatable whether the *Canun* encouraged or hindered medical progress, the fact remains that it represented the chief influence upon Western medicine.

While some of the greatest representatives of Arab medicine in the East were Persians, practically all those of western Arabism, that is of Morocco and Moorish Spain, were Arabs. The most famous of these was Ibn Rushd, or Averroës, better known as a philosopher than as a doctor. However, his *Kulliyyat fa Tibb (Rules of Medicine),* while a compendium of Greek and Arab medicine, is more critical and analytical than either of the comparable works by Ibn Sina and Razi.

It was in the West that the Arabs made one of their most significant discoveries, namely that of contagion. Any doctrine that implies man's isolation from his fellow men and the world at large would obviously be alien to the Muslims. In the comparatively static world of the Greeks, man was considered a more or less self-contained entity, and any illness that might afflict him was born within himself. Viewing man and his position in the universe as they did, Muslims could hardly adhere to such doctrine; and it could hardly have been accidental that they were the first to discover the existence of contagion. They had many occasions to observe contagious diseases, such as smallpox, cholera and bubonic plague. Though they may have been dimly aware of the true nature of these diseases, it was not until the 14th century, at the time of the great plague that ravaged the world from India and Russia across Europe, that they clearly recognized the fact of contagion. This recognition was the great achievement of Ibn Khatib and Ibn Khatima of Granada. Ibn Khatib's most important medical work is called *On the Plague*. We find in it the first clear affirmation of the existence of contagion. Though another two hundred years had to elapse before Gerolamo Fracastoro gave a scientific formulation of contagion, and yet another three hundred before Pasteur's bacteriological discoveries, the fact remains that Ibn Khatib and Ibn Khatima were the first to give clinical accounts of contagion.

Are we entitled, as some Western writers are wont to do, to state that the Arab contribution to medicine does not extend beyond the transmission of Greek learning? Are we to follow them by pointing out the Arab's neglect of surgery and the doubtful effects of Ibn Sina's exaggerated tabulation and pigeonholing of medical knowledge? The recognition of contagion would by itself assure universal significance to Arab medicine. But we find other contributions that go far beyond the discoveries of the Greeks.

In the book *Kitabu'l-Maliki (Liber Regius* in its Latin version) the 10th century al Majusi propounded views that show a rudimentary conception of the capil-

18—A portrait of six Greek physicians found in the Arabic translation of Galen's Treatise on Electuaries (1200 A.D.).

lary system, several hundred years in advance of Western science. In the same century, the geographer and historian al Masudi speaks in his *Kitabu't Tanbih* of the process of evolution from mineral to plant, plant to animal, and animal to man. Modern scholars have recognized in him a forerunner of Darwinism, and the German expert Dieterici called his book about Masudi *Darwinism in the Tenth and the Nineteenth Century* (Leipzig, 1878). Ibn al Nafis, an Arab from Syria or Egypt (d. 1289), discovered not only the fundamental principles of pulmonary circulation, but, by criticizing

Ibn Sina's theory concerning the possible passages of venous blood between the ventricles, established himself as a forerunner of William Harvey.

Last but not least, the Arabs were the first to institute special medical schools with proper examinations, thus paving the way for Europe's later medical faculties. They were also the first to found hospitals, designed and run by experts, and divided into. wards according to the different diseases, thus providing a blueprint for later institutions of a similar kind.

It was hardly surprising that once the light of intellectual objectivity and scientific necessity began to penetrate the darkness in which Europe had lived since the fall of the Roman Empire, Western scholars turned eagerly towards Arab science, finding in it the most vital elements that made the birth of European medicine possible.

19—Avenzoar, (1073-1162 A.D.) an Arab physician who studied carcinoma of the stomach and esophagus.

THE COMPASS LED WEST

HIGH on the list of the more revolutionary contributions of twentieth century science is undoubtedly, the computor, the mechanical robot that does its own 'thinking' in accordance with the automatic reactions determined by the nature of its mechanism. The ancestor of the modern computor is of course the automaton, by dictionary definition 'a mechanical device which acts of itself.'

Now if there is any concoction the creation of which is unrelated to religion it must surely be the automaton, at least within the field of physics and mechanics. Yet even in that sphere Arab creativeness was determined by religious concepts. The purely mechanical interplay of physical forces was felt by them to be close to the substratum of matter and thus very distant from the Deity.

On the whole the ancient Arabs took little interest in 'pure' physics. When, however, these phenomena could be related to functions that were not exclusively mechanical and that illustrated the interplay of forces more obviously linked to the Deity, they considered them as worthy of study. It must be remembered that for the Muslims the universe was a living entity, in fact the visible 'cloak' of God. In consequence, we find the Arabs deeply interested in machines recording the progress of time, for clocks indicate the progressive, that is the living character of the world. The Arabs viewed the world as in a process of continuous becoming (not being) and therefore as an affirmation of God's living concern with it.

Everything that illustrated the world's close ties with its creator was of supreme interest to Muslim scientists. Much of their ingenuity went into the fashioning of 'automata' known as clocks, especially those moved by water, mercury and even by burning candles, for the resulting movement illustrated the interplay between the forces of Nature and the Deity from which they derived their life.

Not only did the Muslims produce several outstanding clocks and automata of various kinds, but also they wrote books about them that became as famous as the objects described. In one of the best known of these books Ridwan describes the water clock constructed in the early thirteenth century by his father, Muhammad ibn Ali. Placed near one of the gates of Damascus, the clock was regarded by Muslims throughout the world as one of the wonders of the world. Perhaps less important, but far more famous, was the water clock presented by Harun al Rashid to Charlemagne in 807.

Among Arab automata the greatest renown was enjoyed by the mechanical toys so beloved by Arab princes and nobles. With these ingenious contraptions the Arabs established a fashion kept alive right up to modern times and personified in the West by Fabergé,

الا انهم يستوحجشون من الطائر وربّيا اخذاجدهم وحمل الى مواضعها الطائر فيبنعها الى العُصَاصة وقال

20—An illustration of three mythological figures from a manuscript by al-Qazwini, 1279 A.D.

the great nineteenth century jeweler who produced an endless variety of beautiful objects for most of the ruling houses of Europe—particularly for the last Russian Tsar. A thousand years earlier Arab specialists produced even more outstanding mechanical 'toys'. When the envoys of Constantine VII of Byzantium visited the Caliph al Muqtadir at Baghdad in 917, nothing impressed them more than the 'Hall of the Tree' in his palace. The goggle-eyed ambassadors beheld a tree made of gold and silver, in the branches of which golden birds moved about chirruping gaily. Yet Western toymakers still feel rather pleased with themselves when they produce a mechanical Mickey Mouse or a doll that shuts and opens her eyes and can say 'mamma'.

Arab scientists turned their attention to graver subjects as well. As early as 860 the three sons of Musa ibn Shakir published the *Book of Artifices* in which a hundred technical constructions are described, including water wells with a fixed level and special vessels for hot and cold water. Among the authors of original scientific books we find one of the earliest Arab philosophers, the famous Kindi, who wrote on specific weight, on optics, light reflection and tides. An even more famous philosopher, Ibn Sina (Avicenna) wrote on the formation of mountains and minerals.

Preoccupation with what might be termed 'living' mechanics drew the Muslims also towards the mysterious powers of the magnet. While the attractive properties of the magnet were discovered by the Greeks, and its directive property by the Chinese, neither of them knew how to utilize those puzzling powers. The Arabs were the first to apply the magnetic needle to navigation. This may have happened as far back as the ninth or tenth century. Even though the first Arab reference to it appears in the 1231 collection of anecdotes by Muhammad al Awfi, long before that date Arab sailors used the compass.

Since optics form a part of the physical sciences, it might be mentioned that modern experts have come to agree that early Muslim optics were far superior to those of medieval Europe. For several centuries Europe relied primarily on an Arab work in that field. This was the *Kitab al Manazir (Opticae Thesaurus)* of Ibn al Haytham of Basra (b. 965), known in Europe as Alhazen. His book influenced scientific thought for at least six centuries. This was hardly surprising since the book combined a wealth of scientific knowledge utterly unknown in the West. Among the great variety of subjects it described we find optical illusions, the structure of the eye, binocular vision, perspective, atmospheric refraction, comets, mirages and, last but not least, the camera obscura, an invention of the author himself.

Ibn Haytham's most revolutionary discovery, however, was that of the true nature of the eye's vision. Opposing the theory of Euclid and Ptolemy according

21—Details of a window of the Alhambra, Granada.

to which vision was due to the rays sent out by the eye
to the object of vision, Ibn Haytham postulated that it
was the object that sent out rays to the eye, in which
its image was produced. "Rather," he wrote, "the form
of the perceived object passes into the eye and is trans-
muted by its transparent body (the lens)." Ibn Haytham influenced not only Roger Bacon, but also Leonardo da Vinci, Johann Kepler and even Descartes, who
without the help of Haytham's discoveries might never
have established his own law of sines. In the universalist
tradition of Arab scientists and thinkers, Ibn Haytham

limited himself not to just one branch of knowledge but made important contributions in the fields of physics, mathematics, physiology, anatomy and meteorology, always seeking affirmations of the living and universalist character of the world.

The Arabs' keen interest in the interrelation between mechanical forces and those that suggested their divine origin inevitably focused their attention on the latent powers of water and its utilization. We still do not know whether they actually invented the water wheel or not; but whoever first thought of it, it was in Arab hands that the water wheel was developed and greatly improved, and it was from Arab lands that it was finally introduced to Europe. Greatly impressed by the famous water wheels that the Crusaders saw in Homs, Antioch and Orontes, on their return to Europe they copied them. They first appeared in Germany.

Anything connected with hydraulics and hydrostatics greatly preoccupied the Arabs, and they were the first to pass on to Europe the relevant facts of Archimedean and Hellenistic mechanics. Their study of these sciences led them also to independent measurements of densities, especially those of metals and precious stones. While they turned to this subject as early as the ninth century—and here mention must be made of such famous men as Razi, al Biruni, Ibn Sina and Omar Khayyam—the standard work was written in the twelfth century by al Khazini. Besides dealing with various physical sciences, the book also contains tables of specific gravities of solids and liquids. Its comprehensiveness is attested by the wide range of its subjects, among which we find theories of gravity, of capillarity, of the lever and the aerometer as well as of balance and of levelling. Like so many of the early Arab books, Khazini's too became the standard textbook of European scientists in the Middle Ages.

Though for many centuries the West either ignored or deliberately kept silent about the scientific findings of the Muslims in general and the Arabs in particular, modern investigations have shown that hardly a single aspect of scientific knowledge had not been discovered by them long before Europe was even aware of its existence. Thus today we know that even the scientific explanation of the rainbow might have Muslim origins. While the door to that explanation was opened already in the tenth century by Ibn Haytham, the law of two refractions and one reflection in spherical drops of water —a law with which Europe credited the Dominican Dietrich of Freiburg—was discovered and formulated earlier by the Muslim Qutb al Din. Likewise we find that some of Leonardo da Vinci's theories of aerial perspective had been anticipated two centuries earlier by Kamal al Din who, incidentally, also postulated that the speed of light, however great, cannot be infinite.

Europe did not become aware of Arab science until after 1085 when Toledo in Spain was conquered by the Christians. It was in that center of Arab studies that, with amazement, Christians were brought face to face with the Arab transmitters of Greek learning and with a storehouse of knowledge that the West had been utterly ignorant of. The Christian scholars of Toledo thus became the first European agents of Greco-Arab science. Since the language in which that science was available to them was Arabic, and very few of them knew that language, they had to rely upon non-Christian helpers.

The first task of the Western scholars was to translate the Arabic manuscripts into Latin. This work was

22—"A couple"—a drawing by Albert Durer (1471-1528).

put into the hands of both Muslim and Jewish natives, some of whom were equally versed in Arabic, Spanish, Hebrew, Latin and even Greek. The initiators of that enormous process were Archbishop Raymond and Archdeacon Dominico Gundisalvi.

But the real father of European Arabism was Gerard of Cremona. He was born in 1114, a time when the center of Arabic knowledge was beginning to pass from the Middle East to Spain and Morocco, the two countries that produced scholars and thinkers as distinguished as Ibn Tufail, Ibn Rushd (Averroës), Ibn Hazm, Idrissi, Ibn Khatib and Ibn Khatima, and the great mystic-philosopher Ibn Arabi. Under Gerard of Cremona's impetus the Arab sciences began to flow unremittingly into Europe, and from his days on the study of the physical sciences at such leading universities as those of Paris, Bologna, Padua and Montpellier was based exclusively on Greco-Arab traditions. This process continued well into the days of the 'high' Renaissance in the sixteenth century.

Since this was the period during which Western civilization and science were finding the direction for their future progress, it seems obvious that our scientific achievements, from compasses to computers, are in some way or another unthinkable without the ancient discoveries of the Arabs.

66

THEY WROTE IN ARABIC

IF IT IS true that for a quarter of a millenium the best of English speech echoed the vocabulary and the lilt of the King James Bible, it is far more true that Arab literature and speech are unthinkable without the Koran, considered by the Muslims not only as beyond compare but also as a miracle, both spiritual and linguistic.

Since Allah spoke to the Prophet Muhammad in Arabic, Arabs venerate their language far more deeply than other nations do theirs. Because Arabic is so impregnated with the spirit of the Koran, its entire way of expression sets it somewhat apart from other languages. And because Arabic is one of the richest and most pliant languages, it is very hard to render into another idiom. In spite of all this, Arab literature has left an indelible mark on the literatures of the West. Though the works of the great Arab poets, from the pre-Islamic ones to a Maari and a Mutanabi, may be known only to Western specialists, a number of Arabic books have greatly influenced Western literature.

One of the most beloved characters in European fiction is undoubtedly Robinson Crusoe, the incarnation of adventure, self-reliance, and nobility of spirit. Few Western readers seem to be aware of Robinson's links with the Arab world. Before he ultimately reached his island, he had been in touch with Arabs, having spent some time in the Moroccan town of Sale as a captive of the famous 'Salli Rovers.' But, apart from this experience, Robinson Crusoe owes the Arabs a debt beyond repayment; for without his Arab progenitor he might never have seen the light of day to fascinate successive generations of young and old readers. The model for Robinson Crusoe was provided by *Hayy ibn Yaqzan (Alive Son of Awake)*, a strange book by the great twelfth century philosopher Ibn Tufail, court doctor of the Almohade sultans at Marrakesh. Whereas Defoe in his *Robinson* is concerned almost entirely with the physical development of his hero, the story of Hayy goes very deep into the nature of human progress from animalism to highest spirituality. Shipwrecked on an uninhabited island as a baby, brought up by a deer, and physically, mentally and spiritually entirely self-taught, Hayy finally reaches sheer mystical insight into the true relationship between man and God. Quite apart from its deeper significance, the book is fascinating simply as a story of adventure; moreover, it can claim to be the first real novel. In 1671 it was translated by the Englishman Pocock into Latin, and in 1708 by Simon Ockley into English. Further English versions appeared in more recent years.

If the impact of Ibn Tufail's novel was limited and slow, that of *The Arabian Nights* was instantaneous and overwhelming. No other Arab book has equally stimulated the advance of Western literature. A collection of separate stories—fabulous, erotic, amusing, and always

علم إذا ما عنـ ـا في حاجبي ولا عيب الا راجي ولست بغي تعليم
لا تشتغلي عنكم و لا أنا لكم بل انـ ـزلت الكرم فادخلوا السبي
للنـاب والاعـد اد للنـاب فانكم رفع الدعوان نحـلا الدعوان والذي يقبل

23—A 13th century illustration of a lady lecturing in a Baghdad mosque.

highly entertaining—the book has Arab, Greek, Persian
and Indian origins. It was finally compiled and unified
by Arab authors (e.g. the tenth century al Jahshiyari)
who gave it an entirely Arab character, placing its two
main centers in Baghdad and Cairo. At times, with the
salty humor of true folk tales, and always with an
astounding inventiveness, the book enjoyed great popularity throughout the Middle East where it was known

chiefly through oral transmission by professional story-tellers. Its popularity with the European public, how-ever, was infinitely greater. The first translation by the Frenchman Galland, in 1704, was soon followed by English versions. Their success was spectacular, and new editions followed one another in the most enviable man-ner of modern best-sellers.

Whence came the extraordinary popularity of the *Arabian Nights?* That popularity becomes intelligible only when we realize that the book acted as a sort of catalyst for the 'Oriental' yearnings that had been grow-ing among Western writers, artists and readers ever since the days of the Crusades. The public found in the *Nights* that element of romance and adventure that was missing from European literature. The stimulus of the *Nights* was partly responsible for the composition of Western books as famous as *Robinson Crusoe* and *Gulliver's Travels.* Arabism, or 'Orientalism,' as it was usually called, provided Western writers with a wealth of new themes. We find such themes in Samuel Johnson's *Ras-selas,* in Byron and Southey, in the satires of Voltaire and of the French reformers, in Beckford's *Vathek,* and in Germany, in Lessing, in Goethe's famous *West-oest-licher Divan*, in Rückert and Platen. The Oriental fashion, in which Arab elements were often confounded with Persian and Indian, persisted through most of the nineteenth century when Victor Hugo could write: 'In the age of Louis XIV all the world was Hellenistic, now it is Orientalist' (Preface to *Les Orientales*). While the *Arabian Nights* by themselves did not create this roman-tic flood, in that process, which greatly widened the scope of European literature and enriched its imagery and language, they provided the focus for Europe's hanker-ing for exoticism and for the latent Oriental interests of its intellectuals.

24—Celebration of the end of Ramadan. Miniature painting by
al-Wasiti, 1237 A.D.

No Western author expressed Europe's fascination with this or that aspect of Arabism in a more dramatic and poetic form than did Shakespeare. Among his most attractive characters two are Arabs or, as he calls them, Moors, Othello and the Prince of Morocco, one of the noblest figures in his *Merchant of Venice*. This prince, modeled on the great Saadien Sultan Ahmed el Mansur, shows a royal dignity expressed in words of great nobility. While the prince addresses Portia, whom he hopes to gain as wife, with the words, 'Mislike me not for my complexion,' he is equally conscious of his 'golden mind' that will not stoop down 'to shows of dross.'

Whereas the Prince of Morocco is but a minor character in the play, Othello completely dominates the drama to which his name is given. A man of unbounded passion, this Moor—"who comes from a land of deserts, rocks and hills whose heads touch heaven" (an obvious reference to the Atlas mountains)—is also a paragon of loyalty, courage, honesty and possessed of a nobility rendered more striking by contrast with the infamy of the 'white' Yago. To the present day, experts acquainted with the Moorish character are amazed at the insight with which Shakespeare delineated Othello. Whence did he derive his astounding knowledge?

In the London of Queen Elizabeth the First, Morocco was very much 'in the news.' Among the founders of the 'Barbary Company,' an association of London merchants trading with Morocco, we find the Earl of Leicester, one of the Bard's patrons; and it was from his many Barbary-merchant friends that Shakespeare obtained much information on Morocco and its people. He also knew Master Roberts who had headed an embassy of the Queen to the Moroccan ruler, and who returned in the company of the Moorish ambassador, Merzouk

دَوَرَّبَا ۞ كُلُّ فِنَّمْ مِنْـهُ طِبْقَهْ ۞ فَاذَا أَبْلَتْ بِأَىِّ فِنِّمْ شِئِتَ تَوَالَ لَكَ

مَا بَعْدَهُ كَوَالِى دَوْرَالْفَلَكَ ۞ وَلَمَّا كَانَتِ الْتَّدَابِيْرُ كُلُّهَا أَعْلَاهَا وَأَسْفَلُهَا

وَفُقَّا عَلَى الْعَالَمِ رَأَيْتُ أَنْ أُبْدِىءَ فِى هَـذَا الشَّكْلِ بِالْعَالَمِ وَمِنْهُ صُوْرَتِهِ كَمَا تَرَى ۞

يَا اسْكَنْدَرُ زَيَّنَ هَـذَا الْكِتَابِ وَمَا بَيِّنَ مَطْلَبِهِ ۞ وَلَوَلَّمَ أُحَصَّلَكَ

غَيْرَ هَـذَا الشَّكْلِ لَكَانَ كَافِيًا ۞ مَنْدَهُ بِنَظَرٍ حَادِقٍ وَفِهْمٍ ثَاقِبٍ يَبَلَّرَنَّكَ

بِأَدْمُرَادِكَ ۞ وَيُقَرَّبُ عَلَيْكَ بُعَّا لَكَ ۞ وَكَلَّا أَذْكَرُنَهُ فِى هَـذَا الْكِتَابِ

25—The Saying on Political Wisdom from al-Muquaddimah by ibn
Khaldun (1332-1406 A.D.)

Raïs. Having watched the ambassador at some of his
many public functions, Shakespeare evidently was struck
by the great nobility of his appearance and demeanor.

Another of Shakespeare's sources of information was
provided by the famous 'condottiere' Sir Anthony Sher-

ley who had visited Morocco on various important missions. Such first-hand information equally served Shakespeare in painting the horrible figure of the Jewish Moor, Aaron, in *Titus Andronicus*, whose model appears to have been a certain Jew from Safi in Morocco whose unsavory story he had learned from his 'Barbary' merchant friends. Altogether we find more than sixty references to Barbary (Morocco) in Shakespeare's plays.

Shakespeare was by no means alone in falling under the spell of Moorish subjects. In his *Tamburlaine the Great* of 1587, Christopher Marlow introduces the 'Kings of Moroccus and Fez.' A year later a certain Ed. White published *A Brief Rehearsal of the Bloody Battle in Barbary;* in 1594, George Peel's play *The Battle of Alcazar* was produced in London, and, shortly afterwards, an anonymous author Ro. C. published a history of Morocco entitled *A True Discourse of Muley Hamet's Death*.

Long before Shakespeare's sixteenth century, we already find Arab influences in European literature. They appear in the poetry of the early Spanish and Provençal troubadours, and, in the thirteenth century, in the French *fabliaux* and *contes*. We find Arab names and Arab settings in the famous *Aucassin et Nicolette,* and Arab echoes even in Boccaccio's *Decamerone*. Chaucer's *Squires Tale* uses a theme brought to Europe by Italian merchants who had traded in the Middle East. And, of course, there is the most famous medieval work of literature, Dante's *Divine Comedy,* replete with details from the story of the Prophet Muhammad's ascension to heaven, and details culled from the *Meccan Revelation* by the great Arab mystic Ibn Arabi. While Europe's 'Arabian fashion' broke into full blossom only after the appearance of the *Arabian Nights,* ever since the days of the Crusades European writers and readers were fascinated by themes found in Arab books, often transmitted only orally.

Arab influences were not limited to 'pure' literature but also extended to historiography. The basis of Arab writings on history was provided by accounts of the life of the Prophet. Since the compilation of such biographies was determined by the Arab system of *isnad*, that is of quoting all available authorities and establishing their reliability, Arab history-writing is distinguished by accuracy rather than by a creative handling of the available materials. It thus provides the modern historian with a most accurate and comprehensive source of material, but offers few works of synthesis and interpretation. And yet the Arabs produced the man whom modern scholars consider as the true father of modern historiography and of the science of sociology. This was Ibn Khaldun.

The fame and importance of Ibn Khaldun rest not so much on his strictly historical works, such as his greater universal history entitled *Book of Examples,* as on his *Muqaddima,* or preface to that work. It is due to this truly revolutionary work that Arnold Toynbee wrote, "Ibn Khaldun has conceived and formulated a philosophy of history which is undoubtedly the greatest work of its kind that has ever yet been created by any mind in any time," and that George Sarton said, "I do not hesitate to call it the most important historical work of the Middle Ages."

While before Ibn Khaldun historiography was concerned mainly with rulers, battles and straightforward accounts of main events, the great Arab thinker was the first to recognize that events did not happen in a vacuum but depended upon an endless variety of factors previously neglected by historians, such as climate, social custom, food, fetishes, and so on. So, in his *Muqaddima* he deals extensively with the subjects of the nature of society and occupation, labor conditions, climate, and best methods of education. Modern scholarship acknowledges that, thanks to him, latter-day historiography has changed fundamentally.

A native of Tunisia, a government official at the Arab courts of Granada, Morocco and Algeria, he became the chief justice of the Mameluke sultans of Egypt, and the first Arab historian to denounce the principles of Aristotle, opposing to these a purely Islamic philosophy. It was in the Maghreb, before settling in the Middle East, that he spent several years in retreat composing his great work—a work that only quite recently appeared in a complete and excellent English translation.

The long years of a foreign colonialism, first Ottoman and then Western, brought Arab creativity to a standstill. But within the last few years there has been a reawakening, and Arab novelists, playwrights, essayists and historians of more than local significance are laying the foundations of a new Arab literature.

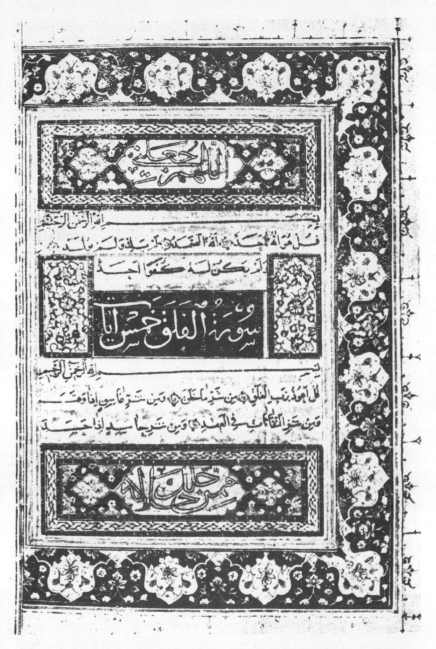

26—A page from a copy of the Koran inscribed by Ya'qut al-Mustasimi,
14th century A.D.

ARABESQUE, ABSTRACTION IN THE ARTS

In one of the most famous paintings of the Italian Renaissance, Fra Lippo Lippi's 'The Coronation of the Virgin,' the angels surrounding the Madonna hold transparent ribbons inscribed with Arab words in praise of Allah. This may seem a surprise to find in one of Christendom's great sacred works of art.

How could this happen? Well, Arab fabrics—silks and brocades—were the most highly prized in Europe, and Arab weavers had to work overtime to meet the mounting demands for them. Many a church vestment used in Christian cathedrals was covered with exquisite designs conjured up by the weavers of Damascus, Cairo and Fez. European artists were as fascinated by these textiles as were their patrons, the princes and bishops, and we find examples of them in the paintings of Christian artists as devout as Giotto and Fra Angelico.

The Arabs had become the world's leading silk mercers and the inventors of various fabrics whose very names proclaim their Arab origin. Among these we find damask, from Damascus; muslin which, under the name of mussolina, was imported from Mosul by Italian merchants, and fustian, originated at Fustat, Egypt's first Islamic capital. When Arab merchants could no longer satisfy Europe's demands for these textiles, Sicily established weaving houses given entirely to copying Arab designs. Silk-weaving begun by Arab craftsmen in Palermo laid the foundations for one of Italy's future most thriving industries.

Arab textile designs consisted usually of arabesque-like arrangements that gradually developed into those of stylized flowers and fruit. It was the arabesque that dominated these designs as it did most of the 'minor' Arab arts.

What is the arabesque and what are its origins? To gain a better comprehension of this most typical feature of Arab art let us compare it with the corresponding aspects of Western art. For the last few thousand years, Western painters and sculptors have been

27—Hispano-Moresque fabric with calligraphic design fróm the 15th century.

trying to 'compete' with God by creating their own world of men and beasts, mountains, rivers and plants. As often as not they also tried to 'tell a story'—historical, moral, religious or social. Inevitably they had to borrow from the arts and sciences that are not, strictly speaking, visual, namely those of the historian, preacher, botanist or novelist. For the proper sphere of the visual artist is that of pure aesthetics, that is, the arrangement of shapes, colors, lines and textures in a given space. Human flesh, the story of Napoleon, a flower or an elephant obviously do not belong to that area.

By the twentieth century the Western artist had lost his faith in mankind and had begun to mistrust and to fear the physical universe with its splitting atom. Moreover, he no longer seemed to care whether he communicated with his fellow-men or not, and withdrew into a private world of his own. He turned away from the visible world and plunged into abstraction, an abstraction that cried out his human despair rather than his creative joy. Western abstract art came to express nothing so much as the '*Angst*' of a century facing the mushroom cloud.

With the advent of Islam, the Arab artist embarked upon abstraction, and he remained faithful to it for over a thousand years. But his abstract art never denoted despair or loss of faith in the visible universe. Rather it was an affirmation of his faith in God and His commandments. The Arab Prophet Muhammad had declared, 'Whosoever makes an image, him will Allah give as a punishment the task of blowing the breath of life into it: but he is not able to do this.' The Prophet's words imply that the fashioning of images is synonymous with competing with God and transgressing His law. So the Arab artist limited himself to abstract themes, and,

80

28—A conception of Archangel Gabriel appearing in a book by
al-Qazwini, 1279 A.D.

in the course of his pursuits, developed what must be
considered the purest art, an art that borrows neither
from history nor literature nor from the other disciplines
that lie outside the range of pure aesthetics.

In the arabesque, which is the crowning expression
of his endeavors, he created an art-form which is abso-
lutely true to the demands of 'pure' art, and which never
tries to be what it is not. He shuns not only 'natural'

objects but also the illusion of perspective, shadow and three dimensions. He remains two-dimensional, and handles exclusively the elements of line, form, space, color and texture. All his imagination thus flows into arrangements of these elements. In their end-product these amount to designs of an ingenuity, geometrical complexity and beauty unequalled by any other attempts at 'pure' art. The order, logic and sense of balance that permeate the arabesque have a classical inevitableness next to which even the greatest paintings of the West appear restless and baroque.

29—Court of the Lions, Alhambra, Granada.

Apart from rare exceptions when the arabesque included stylized plants, even human, and animals (both more common in Persian than in Arab designs), the only 'realistic' element that the Arab artist permitted himself to use was the Arabic script. This he used profusely, often incorporating it into his arabesque. Arabic was for him the language in which God spoke to the Prophet Muhammad, the tongue in which the Koran sings the praise of Allah. Thus its employment represents a praise of God. This application of lettering for decorative purposes was taken over enthusiastically by Europe, and even today we find it on countless churches and secular buildings—from town halls and universities to theaters and banks—throughout the West, usually around the front portals and predominantly in Gothic script. The Arabs themselves carved the combination of arabesque and script on walls whether in stone, alabaster or plaster, and also on ceilings, rafters, doors and shutters. We find it even on tiles.

The arabesque and carved lettering are only two of the many elements of Arab art adopted by Western architecture. Though the Arabs took over the horseshoe arch from the Romans, they gave it the definite form which became a prominent feature of their architecture and was avidly copied by the West. They gave us also the cusped, trefoil and ogee arches, and thus provided the model for the Tudor arch and other arches found chiefly·in English, French and Italian churches. It is the Muslim minaret, itself inspired by the Greek light-house, that was to appear in Europe in the form of the campanile, the most famous example of which can be seen in the San Marcus square in Venice, and in innumerable towers on buildings, the best known of which is probably that rising from the Palazzo Vecchio in Florence.

The use of different-colored bands of marble on the facades of buildings, forming so conspicuous a feature of some of the finest Italian churches, was first introduced by the Arabs. The fine brick tracery of the Giralda tower in Seville, and of its sister minarets, the Kutubia and Hassan's Tower in Morocco, can be found in Gothic tracery in Europe—for example on the Bell Tower at Evesham in England. The elegant cranellations on the roofs of some of the finest palazzi in Venice owe their

30—Glass lantern from the mosque of an-Nasir Muhammad, Cairo
(1330 A.D.)

existence to Arab models. Strangely enough, the medallions of Christian saints that beautify the Norman Capella Palatina in Palermo bear inscriptions in Kufic, the early Arabic script.

Limiting himself to non-representational subjects, the Arab artist neglected the arts of painting and sculpture. He concentrated on what are called the 'minor arts,' but raised these to the status of major arts. A piece of pottery from Valencia, an Egyptian crystal

84

carving or a Syrian beaker reveals as much ingenuity and technical skill as does any Western painting or piece of sculpture.

The earliest known pieces of Arab pottery date from the 9th century. Since few Arab countries possessed the fine-grained and more vitreous kaolin clay essential for the making of fine porcelain, they concentrated on pottery (known usually as faience or majolica) which could be manufactured from a coarse-grained, porous clay. Arab pottery enjoyed a great renown among European connoisseurs, and many Christian princes commissioned Arab potters to produce for them articles for display. Particularly popular were the *azulejos*—the iridescent lustre pottery that came from Egypt, Syria, and particularly the Moorish kilns in Valencia.

Even better known were articles that bore the erroneous name of 'Chinese blue.' This blue was not a Chinese, but an Arab invention. The Chinese imported the requisite ingredients from the Middle East, and called the end product 'Muhammadan blue.' As late as the 17th century, Dutch traders used to import Arab-produced 'Chinese blue' pottery, passing it off as Chinese. The impact of that pottery can be seen to the present day in the blue wares of Delft in Holland, and Copenhagen in Denmark. Though the Arabs did not actually invent the glazed tiles, they perfected and popularized them. Some of the tiles of Syria, the Maghreb and other Arab areas have been surpassed in design, color and glaze not even by Chinese tiles.

If Renaissance Europe was an avid buyer of Arab pottery, it was even more eager to procure Arab glasswares, especially those of Syria. Both princes and churches were proud to possess Syrian lamps, beakers and bottles covered with *repoussé* work and enamel.

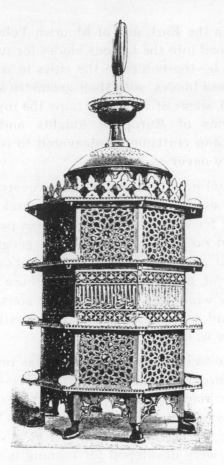

**31—A chandelier from the mosque of Sultan Hassan, Cairo
(1363 A.D.)**

From the 15th century on, European artisans, especially
in Venice, tried to emulate these wares, without, however, achieving their perfection. It was due to these
beginnings that Venice, rather nearby Murano, became
one of the world's centers for the manufacture of luxury
glass.

The high standards of Arab craftsmanship impressed
Europe in practically all the domains of the 'minor' arts.
Pride of place belonged to metal work. The flexible steel

of Damascus in the East, and of Moorish Toledo in the West, was formed into the famous blades for swords and rapiers known by the names of the cities in which they originated. These blades, with their geometrical or floral designs in gold, silver or copper became the much treasured possessions of European knights and princes. Though European craftsmen endeavored to reach their perfection, they never succeeded.

Less martial in nature, but equally coveted in Europe, were the ewers, salvers and jewel-cases inlaid in gold and silver for which Mosul in Iraq was particularly renowned. And no Western astronomer, geographer or sea captain felt perfectly at ease in his work unless he possessed one of the Arab astrolabes, those beautiful instruments by which the position of the stars could be ascertained, and without which, in compass-less days, navigation was well nigh impossible.

One of the 'minor' Arab arts that has retained its high prestige throughout the world to the present day is that of leather manufacture. Even today Western producers of leather goods call their finest articles 'Morocco' leather. For it was in Morocco where, at a very early date, methods were developed for tanning hides (especially goatskin) almost to the softness of silk, and dyeing the leather with vegetable dyes that retained their color almost indefinitely. The Arab leather-craft that left its deepest mark upon Europe was that of bookbinding. With its gold tooling, its colored panels sunk into the leather and its protective flaps, Arab bookbinding was much imitated in Venice and Florence where Arab-style bindings and other leather articles are being produced to the present day.

DATE DUE

The Arab arts provide a notable example of the spirit that dominated Arab culture in general. That culture seldom, if ever, indicated a divorce from religion. Rather it affirmed man's willing submission to the will of God (which, in fact, is the meaning of the word Islam) and his joyful acceptance of the divine law.